Piano Exam Pieces

ABRSM Grade 4

Selected from the 2017 & 2018 syllabus

Name

M000168117

Date of exam

Contents

Editor for ABRSM: Richard Jones

Other pieces for Grade 4

LIST A

4   **Clementi** Allegretto: 1st movt from Sonatina in G, Op. 36 No. 2. *Encore*, Book 2 (ABRSM) or Clementi, Sonatinas, Op. 36, 37, 38 (ABRSM)

5   **Kirchhoff** Courante. *Piano Lessons*, Book 2 (Faber)

6   **Kuhlau** Allegro: 1st movt from Sonatina in C, Op. 55 No. 1. Kuhlau, *Sonatinas*, Vol. 1 (Peters) or No. 11 from *Das neue Sonatinenbuch*, Vol. 1 (Schott)

LIST B

4   **Gurlitt** Klage: No. 18 from Gurlitt, *24 melodische Etüden*, Op. 201 (Zen-On)

5   **George Nevada** Ninette's Musette: No. 5 from George Nevada, *Romantic Impressions* (Schott) or *Waltzes – 48 Original Piano Pieces* (Schott)

6   **Tchaikovsky** Mazurka: No. 11 from *Album for the Young*, Op. 39 (ABRSM) or No. 19 from *A Keyboard Anthology*, 2nd Series, Book 1 (ABRSM)

LIST C

4   **Kabalevsky** In the Gymnasium: No. 3 from *Four Little Pieces*, Op. 14. Kabalevsky, *Easy Piano Compositions* (Boosey & Hawkes)

5   **R. Lane** The Penguin: No. 3 from *Talent Night at the Zoo* (Editions BIM)

6   **Elissa Milne** Foreign Correspondent: from *Pepperbox Jazz*, Book 2 (Faber)

First published in 2016 by ABRSM (Publishing) Ltd,
a wholly owned subsidiary of ABRSM, 24 Portland Place,
London W1B 1LU, United Kingdom
© 2016 by The Associated Board of the Royal Schools of Music
Distributed worldwide by Oxford University Press

Music origination by Julia Bovee
Cover by Kate Benjamin & Andy Potts
Printed in England by Page Bros (Norwich) Ltd,
on materials from sustainable sources.
Reprinted in 2016

Minuet and Trio

Second movement from Sonata in A flat, Hob. XVI:43

Joseph Haydn
(1732–1809)

Haydn's reputation has long rested largely on his symphonies and string quartets, but it is now widely recognized that his piano sonatas are of comparable importance. He composed over 60 sonatas during a period of roughly 35 years (c.1761–95). Haydn moved to Esterháza, Hungary, in 1766 and around the same time discovered the keyboard music of C. P. E. Bach. Later he saw these two events as crucial for his development as a composer. The relative isolation of Esterháza encouraged him to be original, and in C. P. E. Bach he found a model for music of great depth and emotional profundity.

The Sonata in A flat (Hob. XVI:43), whose middle movement is selected here, belongs to the period after these events had taken place. It is thought to date from around 1771–3, and was first published in London in 1783, probably without the composer's knowledge. Haydn used the wedge (bb. 0–2) to indicate normal staccato, not staccatissimo. Dotted-rhythm figures of this kind might be played staccato throughout. All dynamics are editorial suggestions only. Only the right-hand slurs in bb. 10–11, 19–21, 24–7 and 31–3 are present in the source; the remainder are editorial.

Source: first edition, *A Fifth Sett of Sonatas for the Piano Forte or Harpsichord* (London: Beardmore & Birchall, 1783)

Fine

Trio

D.C. al Fine

Prelude on 'Jesus, My Joy'

Praeambulum supra Jesu, meine Freude

KWV 502

J. L. Krebs
(1713–80)

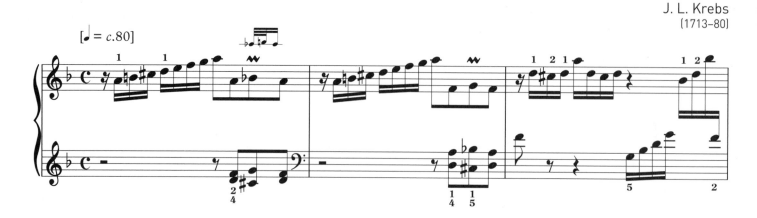

The German composer and organist Johann Ludwig Krebs first had music lessons with his father Johann Tobias Krebs. In 1726 he enrolled at the St Thomas School in Leipzig, became a member of the St Thomas Church choir, and started having lessons with J. S. Bach. In 1729 he became one of Bach's chief assistants, copying out music and playing the harpsichord in the collegium musicum (music society) that Bach directed. In later years he was employed as an organist – at St Mary's, Zwickau (from 1737), at the Castle Church, Zeitz (from 1744), and at the court of Altenburg (from 1756).

Krebs's *Clavier Übung* (Keyboard Practice) contains all the best-known Lutheran chorales (hymns), each treated in three different ways: a praeambulum (prelude), only very loosely based on the chorale melody (as in the piece selected here); a plain chorale with florid bass; and a plain chorale with figured bass. Dynamics are left to the player's discretion.

Source: *Erste Lieferung der Clavier Übung bestehend in verschiedenen Vorspielen und Veraenderungen einiger Kirchen Gesaenge* (Nuremberg: Balthasar Schmid, n.d.)

Allegretto

Second movement from Sonatina in A, Op. 41 No. 12

J. B. Vanhal
(1739–1813)

The Czech composer Johann Baptist Vanhal played the violin, cello and organ, and composed over 700 instrumental works, more than 70 symphonies and around 60 masses. He studied with Dittersdorf in Vienna, where he established himself as a successful composer and teacher (his pupils included Pleyel). From 1769 to 1771 he travelled in Italy.

The Allegretto from Vanhal's Sonatina in A, selected here, illustrates his attractive, rather Mozartian style. The piece is cast in rounded binary form – A, B (b. 17), A¹ (b. 34) – plus a substantial coda (b. 51). The indication *dolce* also implies 'softly'. Left-hand crotchets, plus the right-hand crotchets in the coda, might be played staccato (i.e. as quavers) in order to preserve the lightness of touch that is appropriate to this piece. The second slur in b. 7 and the tempo marks in bb. 32–34 are editorial additions.

Source: *12 Sonatines facilées et progressifes pour le Piano-Forte*, Op. 41 (Mayence: Schott, 1808)

B:1

Scherzo

No. 7 from *Skizzen*, Op. 77

Heinrich Hofmann
(1842–1902)

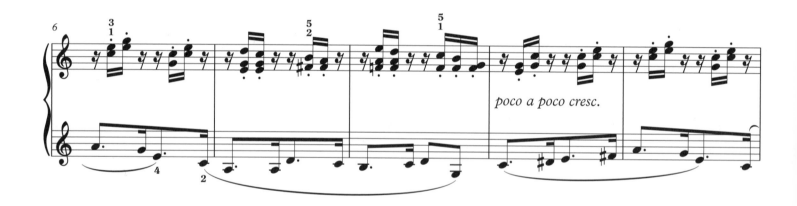

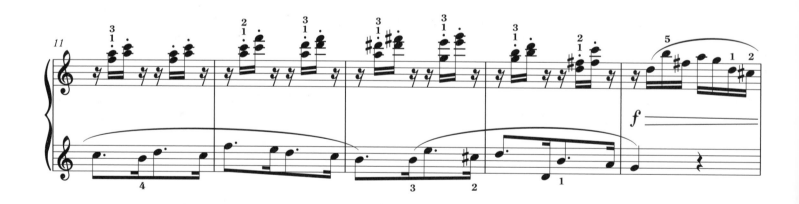

Heinrich Hofmann was a German composer and pianist who became a cathedral chorister at the age of nine and entered Kullak's Neue Akademie der Tonkunst (New Academy of Music), Berlin, at the age of fifteen. He then began to teach and play the piano professionally. Nowadays he is best known for his chamber music and keyboard pieces. *Skizzen* (Sketches), Op. 77, from which No. 7 is selected here, contains 20 pieces, all with programmatic or genre titles. In this Mendelssohn-like Scherzo, all pedal marks are editorial suggestions only.

Source: *Skizzen: 20 kleine melodiöse Klavier-Stücke*, Op. 77 (Leipzig: Carl Rühle, n.d.)

The Merry Peasant, Returning from Work

Fröhlicher Landmann, von der Arbeit zurückkehrend

No. 10 from *Album für die Jugend*, Op. 68

Robert Schumann
(1810–56)

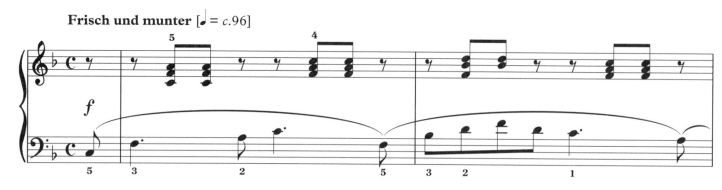

Robert Schumann's *Album für die Jugend* (Album for the Young), from which this piece is selected, was composed in less than a month in 1848. At the time, the composer wrote: 'I don't remember ever having been in such good musical form…the pieces simply poured out, one after another.' Some of the 42 pieces in the collection were dedicated to Schumann's daughter Marie on her seventh birthday.

Schumann's markings make it clear that the opening phrase and its repeats are to be played *forte*. However, to create a degree of light and shade, the phrases at bb. 9–10 and 15–16 might be played at a lower dynamic level.

Source: *43* [sic] *Clavierstücke für die Jugend*, Op. 68 (Hamburg: Schuberth & Co., 1850)

B:3

Waltz in A

Arvīds Žilinskis
(1905–93)

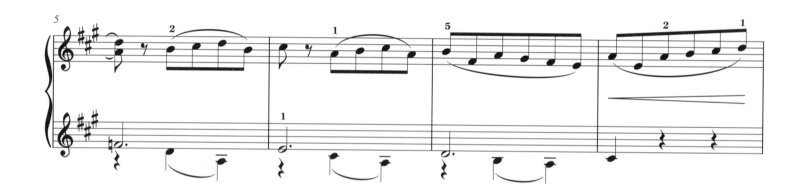

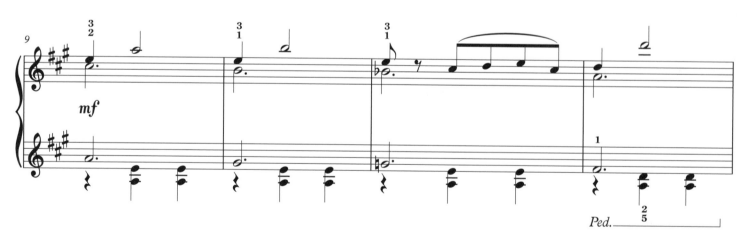

The Latvian composer and pianist Arvīds Žilinskis was the son of a farmer and grew up in a rural environment, often helping his father to herd his cattle and horses. He began learning the piano when displaced to southern Ukraine at the end of the First World War. On his return to Latvia, he entered the Riga Conservatory at the age of 15. Following his graduation in 1933 he started to give concerts in schools, and wrote numerous songs and piano pieces that became very popular with children. Many of these pieces reflect his love of the Latvian countryside. He taught for many years at the Latvian Conservatory, and in all composed over 1,500 works, including ballets and operettas.

The piece selected here – Valsis (Waltz) – is a slow waltz in A major. It falls into ABA *da capo* form, with a central B section in the relative minor F sharp.

Reproduced by permission. All enquiries about this piece, apart from those directly relating to the exams, should be addressed to Musica Baltica, Kr. Barona iela 39, Riga LV-1011, Latvia.

Alarm

Uzbuna

from *Na velikom brodu*

C:1

Bruno Bjelinski
(1909–92)

The Croatian composer Bruno Bjelinski was born in Trieste and studied law and composition in Zagreb. He taught at the Zagreb Academy of Music for over 30 years (1945–77). His piano collection *Na velikom brodu* (On the Great Ship), from which this piece is selected, was composed in 1961. Although the published metronome mark is ♩ = 144, candidates may wish to choose a more relaxed tempo, for example ♩ = *c.*112.

C:2

Bow-Chicka-Wow-Wow

No. 7 from *Cool Beans!*, Vol. 2

Ben Crosland
(born 1968)

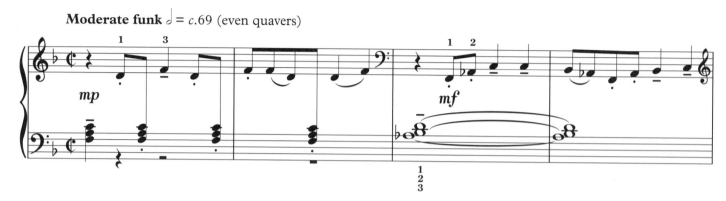

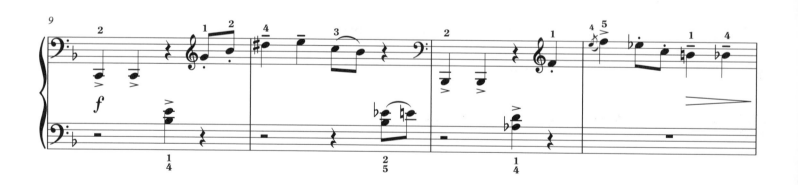

As a teenager, Ben Crosland developed a strong interest in composition and synthesis, and has since experimented with various compositional styles. He began his teaching career in 1987, and has found fulfilment as a composer in writing educational music for his piano pupils, mostly in jazz and popular styles. He runs a music school, 'The Music Grove', in his home town of Worcester.

The composer has written: 'In this piece I have tried to capture the feel of funky, wah-wah guitar. Tempo must be absolutely solid throughout: be careful not to take it too fast, or the right-hand jumps become too difficult. For an instant wah-wah piano effect, your audience might try *gently* flapping the palms of their hands over their ears as they listen. (I do not recommend asking your examiner to do this, however!)'

© Editions Musica Ferrum and Ben Crosland 2013

All enquiries about this piece, apart from those directly relating to the exams, should be addressed to Editions Musica Ferrum at info@musica-ferrum.com, or to the composer at enquiries@bencrosland.co.uk

Очи чёрные   Ochi chërnye

Black Eyes

Arranged by Moira Hayward

Trad. Russian

This is a piano arrangement of a traditional Russian song, whose music is apparently related to a piece entitled *Valse hommage* by Florian Hermann, published in 1884. The lyrics (published in 1843) by the Ukranian poet Yevhen Hrebinka, begin as follows:

Black eyes, passionate eyes,
Burning and beautiful eyes!
How I love you, how I fear you.
It seems I met you in an unlucky hour!